LEVEL 4

A LINE A DAY
SIGHT READING

MW00582994

By Jane Smisor Bastien

Preface

A Line a Day Sight Reading, Level 4 reinforces the concepts from Bastien Piano Basics, Piano, Level 3 (WP203).

Each page has two parts:
• a line of notes, intervals, or chords ("Daily Note Search") to name and play in the correct place on the keyboard. These are random note examples and may be played with any fingers.
• three four-measure phrases to sight read. A variety of bass accompaniments are included in the reading exercises as well as triads and inversions, octaves, and triplets. Five finger positions in Db, Ab, and Eb are used as well as scale studies in C, G, F, D, A, E, Db, Ab, Eb, and A and D minor.

It is recommended that the student complete the "Daily Note Search" *each* day and then play *one* four-measure phrase correctly with as little "practice" as possible. Specific directions are given on page 2. Transposition of the four-measure phrases may be assigned if desired.

The following Level 3 books are suggested for further sight reading.

Favorite Classic Melodies (WP75)
Duet Favorites (WP62)
Popular Hymns (WP229)
Popular Christmas Songs (WP223)
Christmas Duets (GP313)
Boogie, Rock and Country (WP240)
Pop Piano Styles (WP53)
Pop Rock 'N Blues - Book 2 (GP38)
3rd Parade of Solos (WP244)
4th Parade of Solos (WP245)
Piano Recital Solos (WP77)
Bastien Favorites (GP85)
More Folk Tunes for Fun (GP26)
Indian Life (WP234)
Dinosaur Kingdom (WP246)
Hebrew Favorites (GP92)
Japanese Folk Tunes (GP91)
Playtime at the Piano - Book 2 (GP19)
Space Adventures (WP236)

About the Composer

Jane Smisor Bastien teaches pre-schoolers through advanced high school students in her La Jolla, California, home studio. She is very active in the San Diego music teacher organizations.

For many years Mrs. Bastien was director of the Preparatory Department at Tulane University in New Orleans. It was for her students there that she first started writing. Since then she and her husband, James, have produced music and methods for all ages.

ISBN 0-8497-9499-4

WP263

Daily Note Search

Name and play the notes in the correct place on the keyboard, holding each note for its exact value.

Before You Sight Read Each Phrase

1. What is the key signature?
2. What is the time signature?
   Write the counts in the book.
3. Look through the entire piece and try to discover any possible problem spots.
4. Notice the dynamics, slurs, and ties.
5. Find the hand position.
   What is the first note in the right hand?
   What finger goes on that note?
   What is the first note in the left hand?
   What finger goes on that note?
6. Set the tempo by counting one measure aloud and then play on the next "one." Play slowly enough so you can think about everything and keep a steady tempo.
   Counting aloud with the metronome (♩ = 50) will help you keep a steady beat.

Evaluate Your Sight Reading

1. Did you play the correct notes?
2. Did you play straight through in the correct rhythm and keep a steady tempo?
3. Did you count aloud as you played?
4. Did you lift your hands to "breathe" at the ends of the slurs?
5. Did you observe the dynamics?

*Keep a Record of Your Progress

1. In the first box write the day, or date, you read this phrase.
2. In the second box keep track of how many times it took you to play the phrase correctly. Put a ✔ for each time.
3. Your goal is to have as few checks as possible. Concentration will save practice time!

For example:

Daily Note Search

1.

| Day or Date | Number of Times Played |

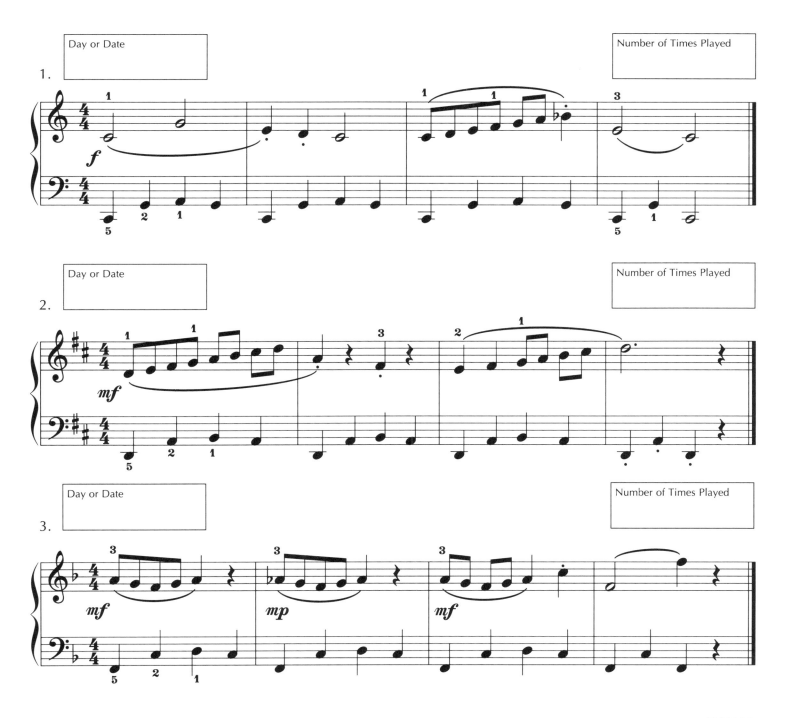

2.

| Day or Date | Number of Times Played |

3.

| Day or Date | Number of Times Played |

WP263

Daily Note Search

Day or Date

Number of Times Played

4.

Day or Date

Number of Times Played

5.

Day or Date

Number of Times Played

6.

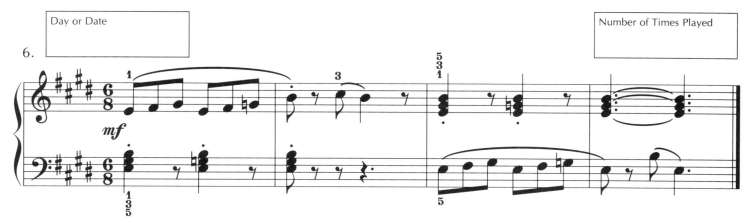

Daily Note Search

After you have sight read each line a day as usual, play lines 7, 8, and 9 without stopping.

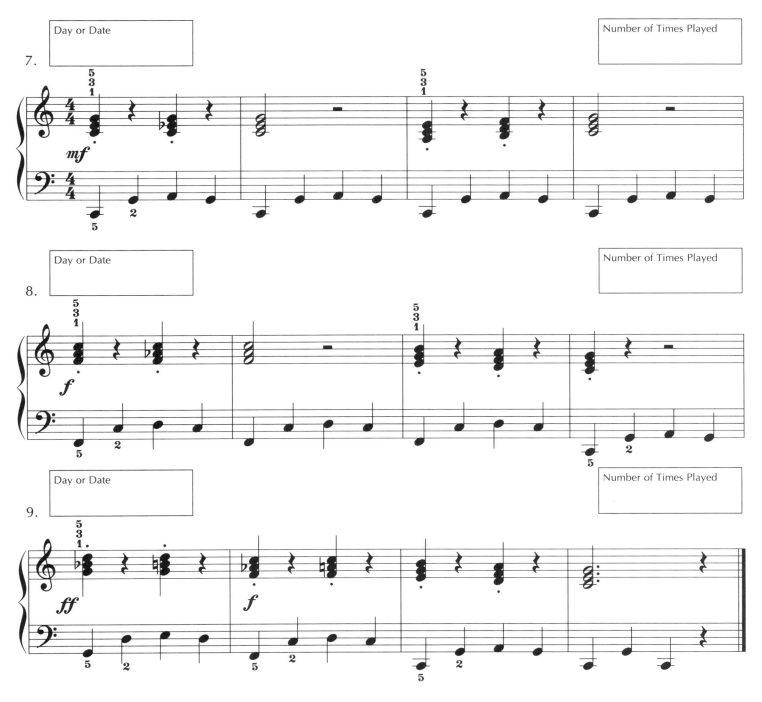

Daily Note Search

Daily Note Search

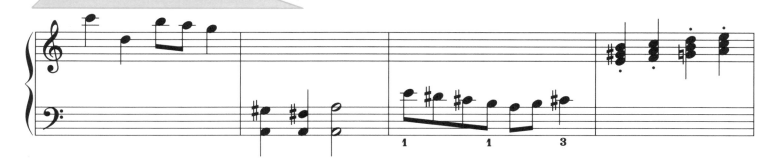

After you have sight read each line a day as usual, play lines 13, 14, and 15 without stopping.

Day or Date	Number of Times Played

13.

Day or Date	Number of Times Played

14.

Day or Date	Number of Times Played

15.

Daily Note Search

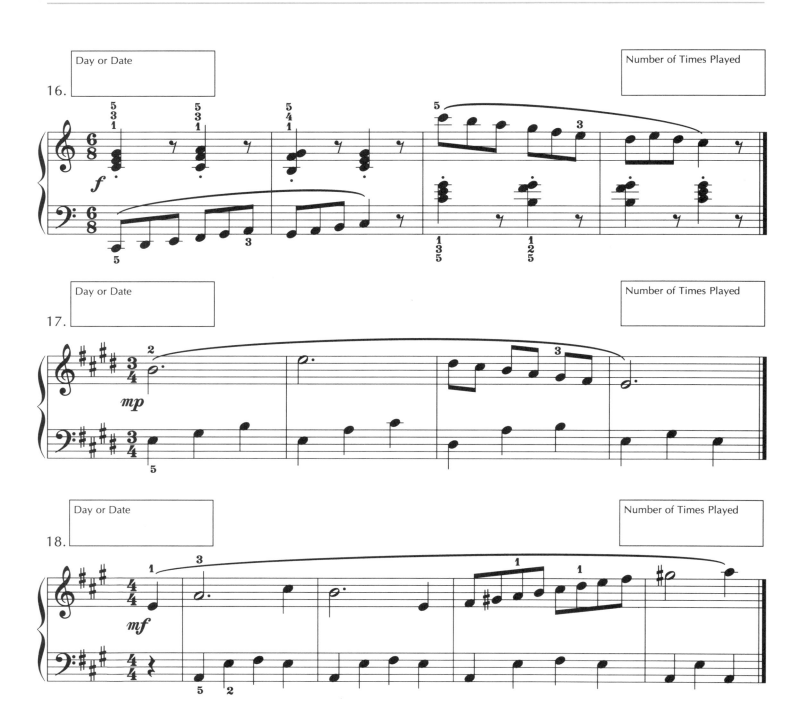

Day or Date

Number of Times Played

16.

Day or Date

Number of Times Played

17.

Day or Date

Number of Times Played

18.

Daily Note Search

After you have sight read each line a day as usual, play lines 19, 20, and 21 without stopping.

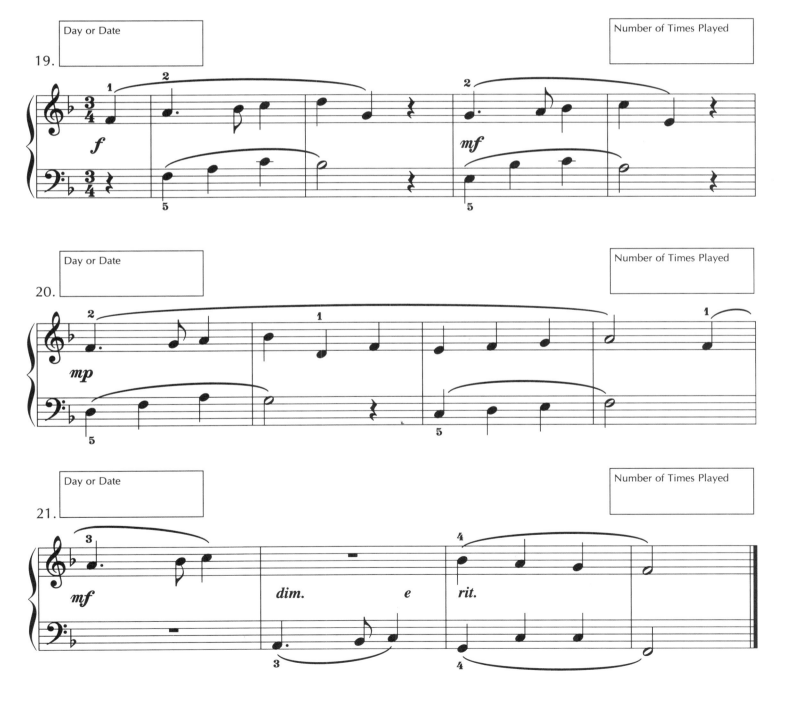

Daily Note Search

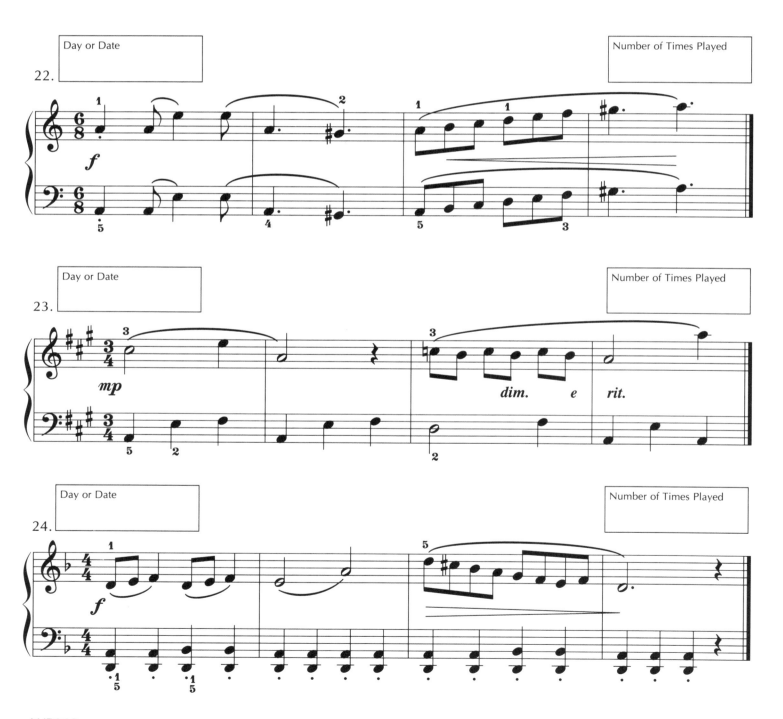

Daily Note Search

After you have sight read each line a day as usual, play lines 25, 26, and 27 without stopping.

12

Daily Note Search

Day or Date

Number of Times Played

28.

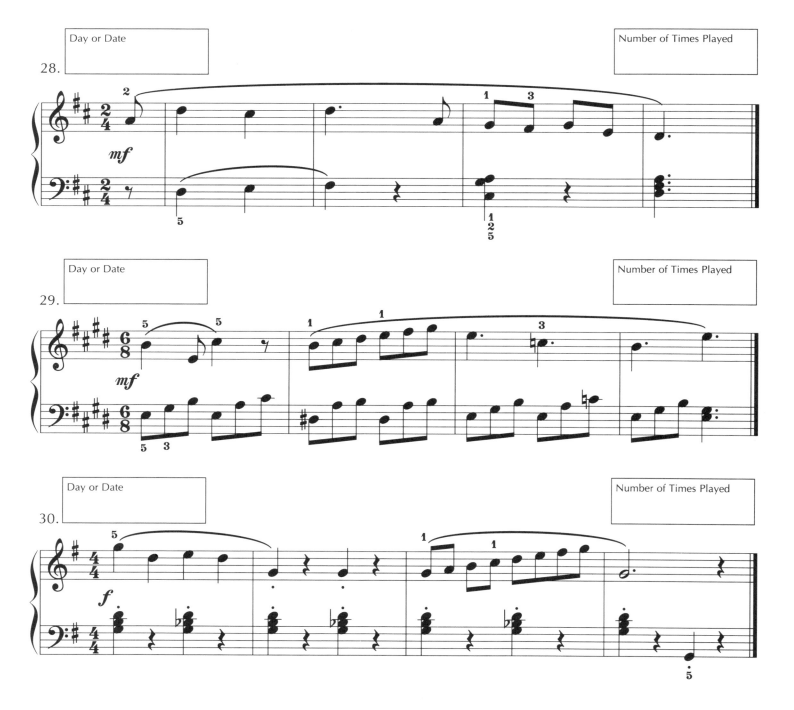

Day or Date

Number of Times Played

29.

Day or Date

Number of Times Played

30.

WP263

Daily Note Search

Daily Note Search

Day or Date

Number of Times Played

34.

Day or Date

Number of Times Played

35.

Day or Date

Number of Times Played

36.

Daily Note Search

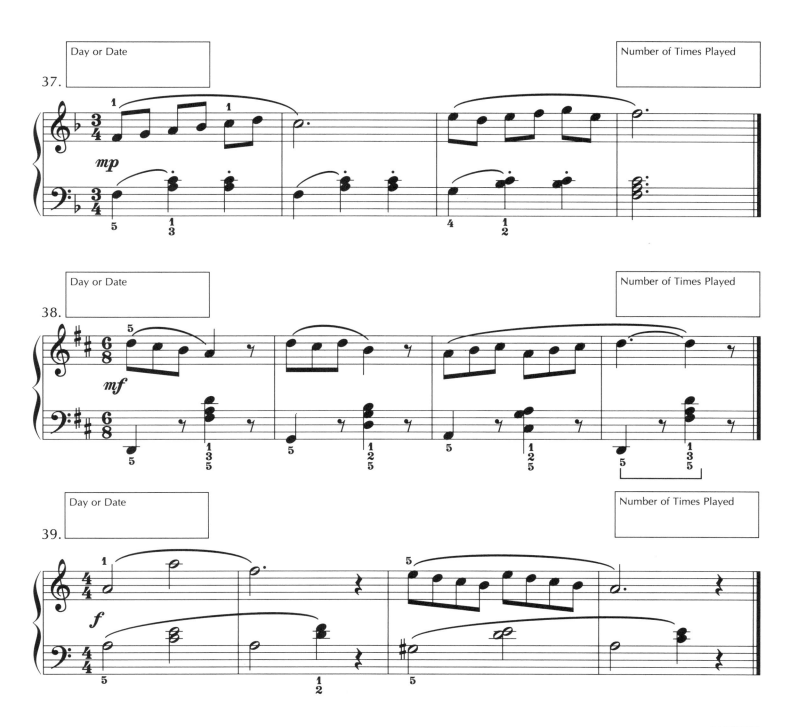

Day or Date		Number of Times Played

37.

Day or Date		Number of Times Played

38.

Day or Date		Number of Times Played

39.

Daily Note Search

Day or Date		Number of Times Played

40.

Day or Date		Number of Times Played

41.

Day or Date		Number of Times Played

42.

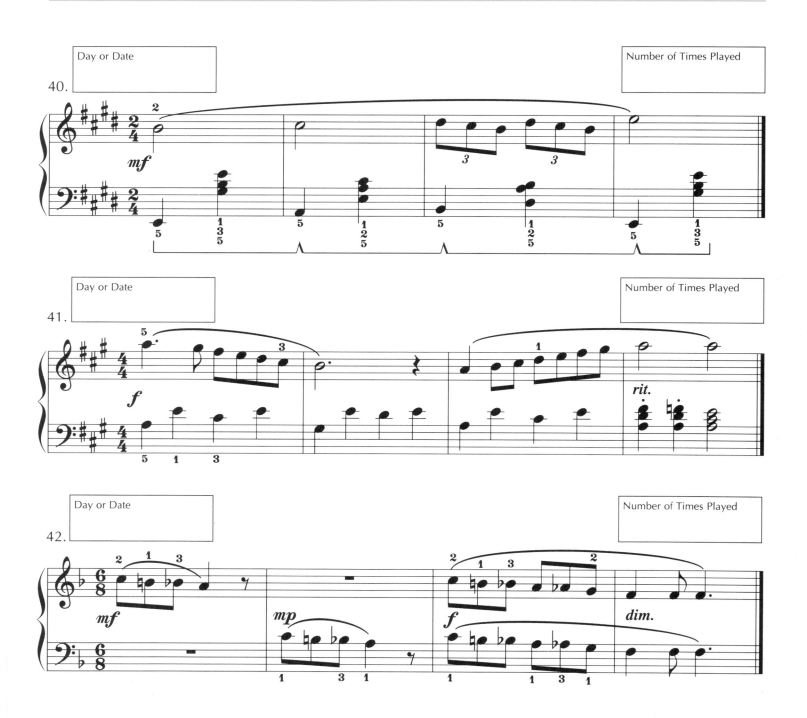

Daily Note Search

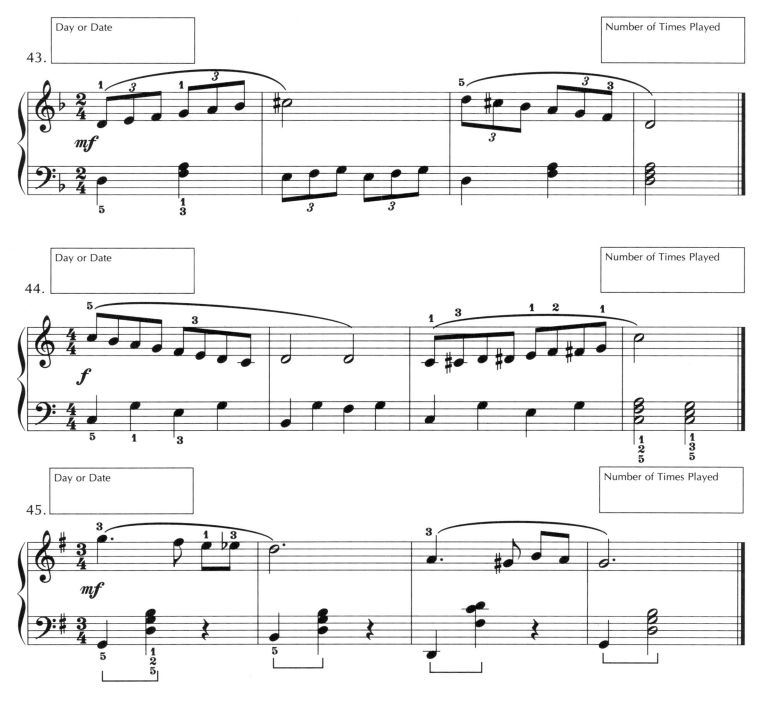

Daily Note Search

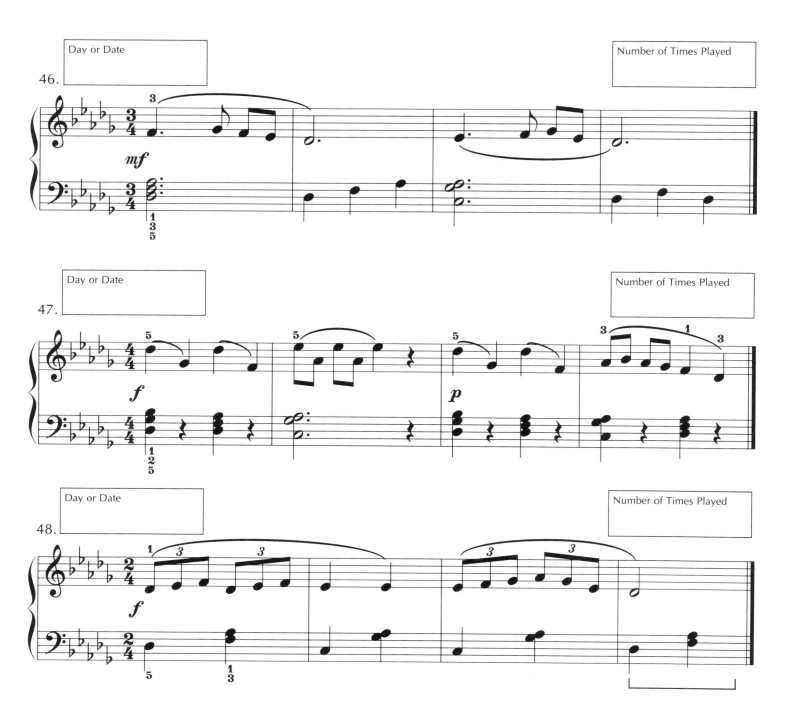

Daily Note Search

After you have sight read each line a day as usual, play lines 49, 50, and 51 without stopping.

Daily Note Search

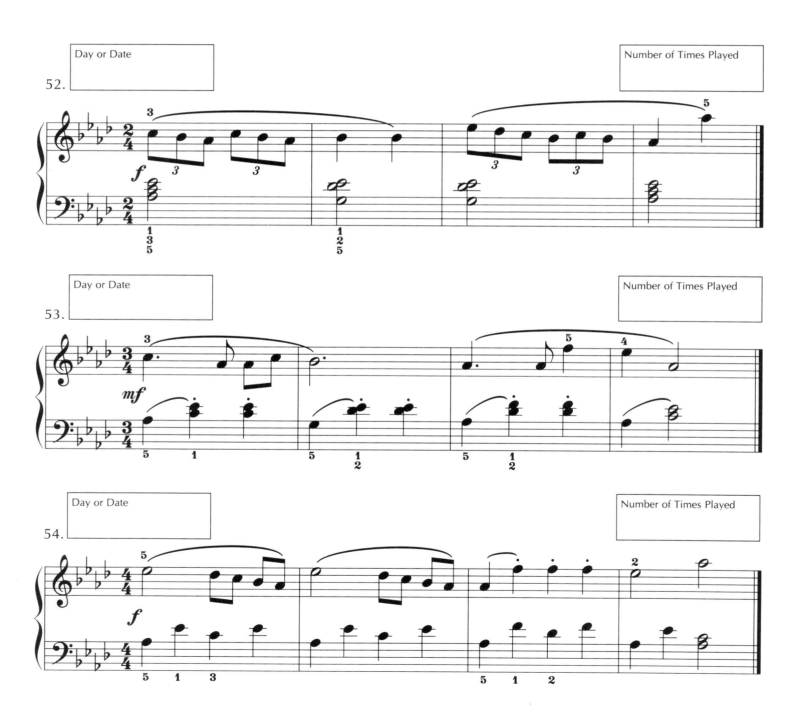

52.

Day or Date

Number of Times Played

53.

Day or Date

Number of Times Played

54.

Day or Date

Number of Times Played

Daily Note Search

After you have sight read each line a day as usual, play lines 55, 56, and 57 without stopping.

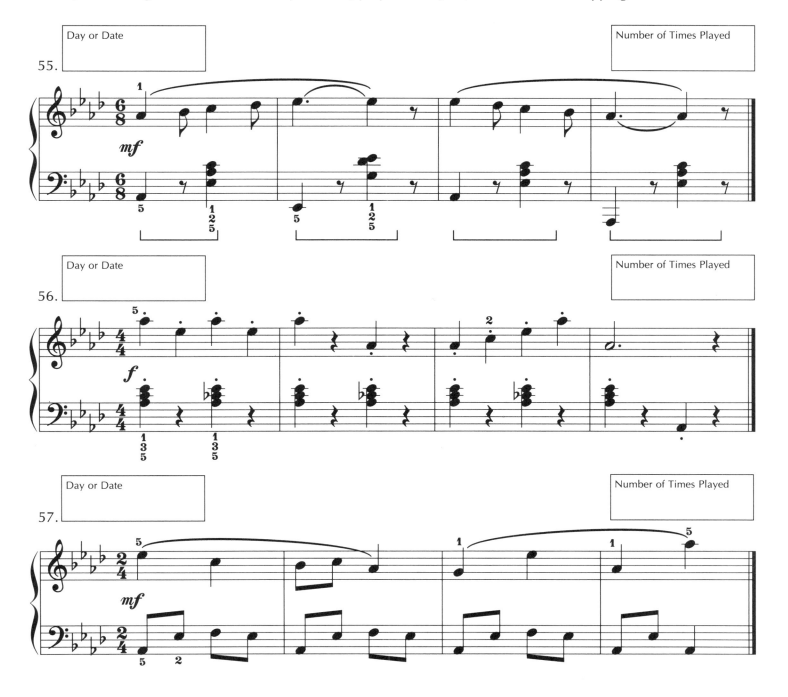

Daily Note Search

Day or Date

Number of Times Played

58.

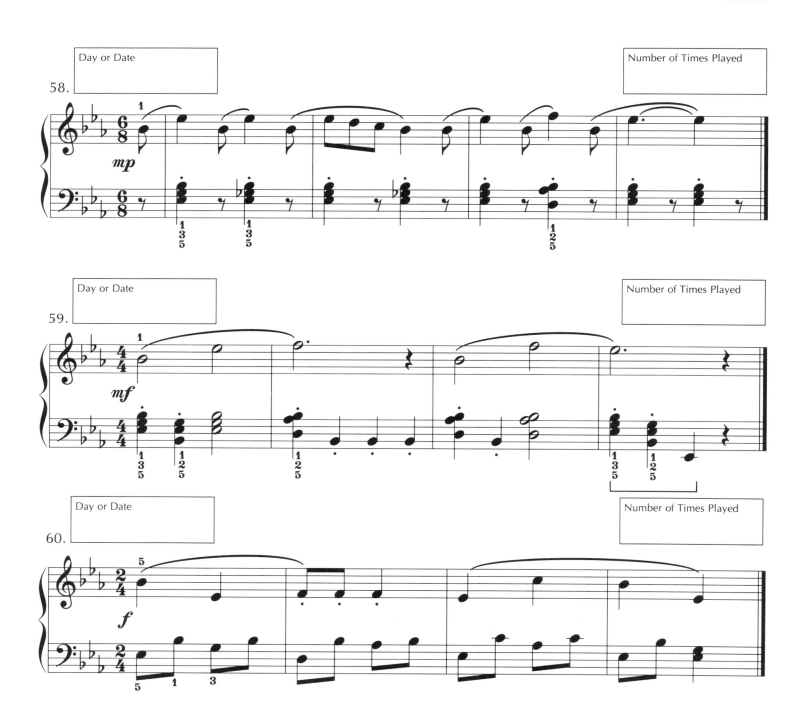

Day or Date

Number of Times Played

59.

Day or Date

Number of Times Played

60.

Daily Note Search

After you have sight read each line a day as usual, play lines 61, 62, and 63 without stopping.

61.

Day or Date	Number of Times Played

62.

Day or Date	Number of Times Played

63.

Day or Date	Number of Times Played

Daily Note Search

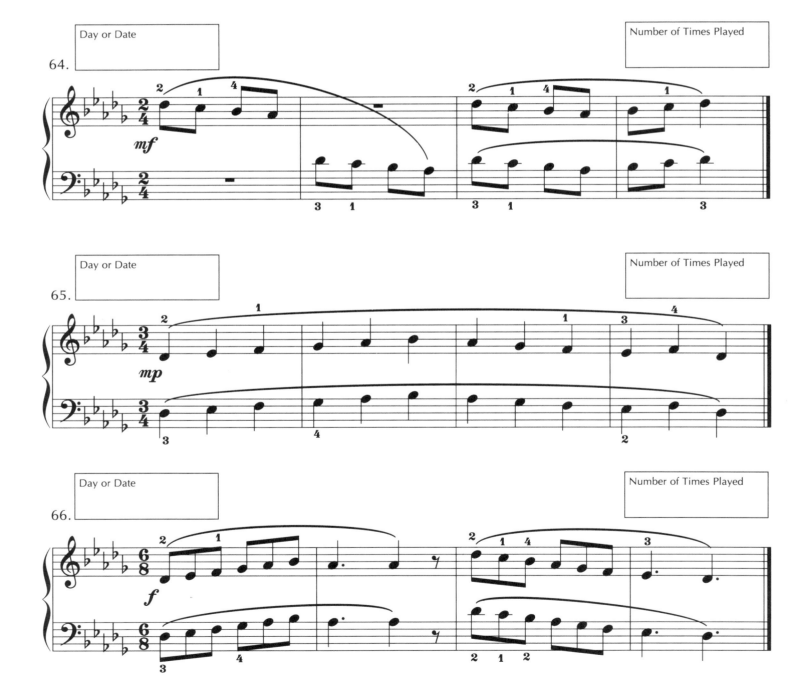

Day or Date		Number of Times Played

64.

Day or Date		Number of Times Played

65.

Day or Date		Number of Times Played

66.

Daily Note Search

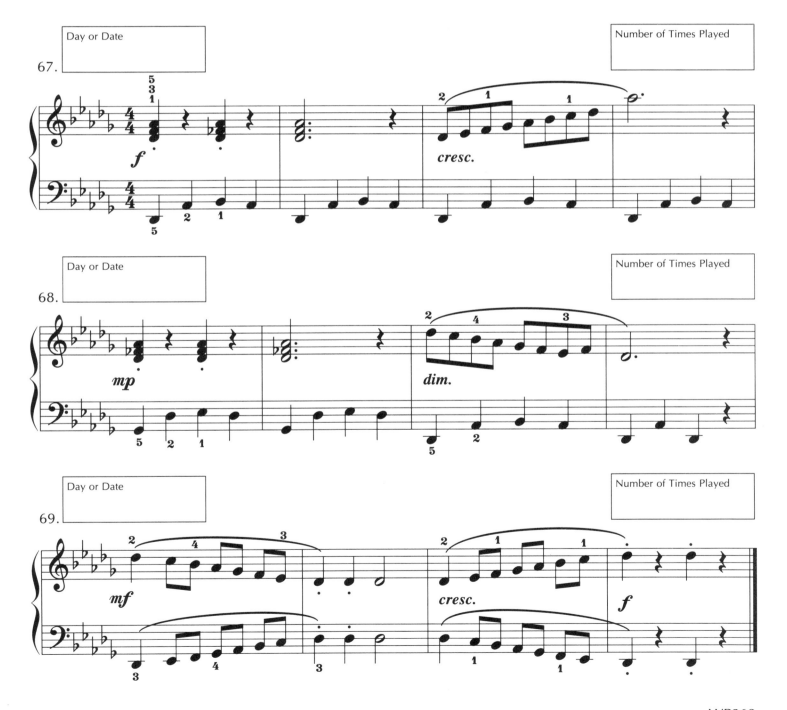

After you have sight read each line a day as usual, play lines 67, 68, and 69 without stopping.

67.

Day or Date

Number of Times Played

68.

Day or Date

Number of Times Played

69.

Day or Date

Number of Times Played

Daily Note Search

Day or Date

Number of Times Played

70.

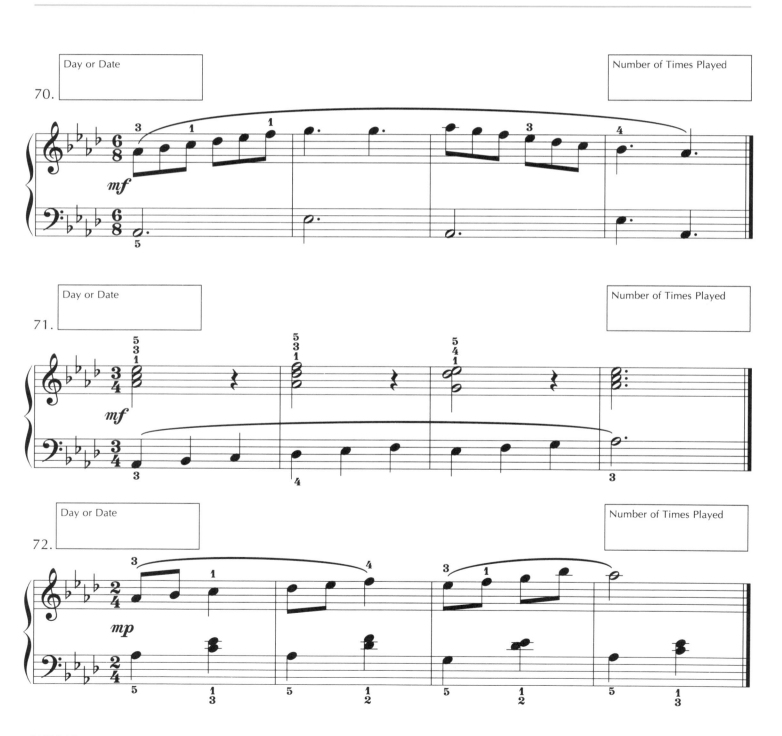

Day or Date

Number of Times Played

71.

Day or Date

Number of Times Played

72.

WP263

Daily Note Search

After you have sight read each line a day as usual, play lines 73, 74, and 75.

Day or Date	Number of Times Played

73.

74.

75.

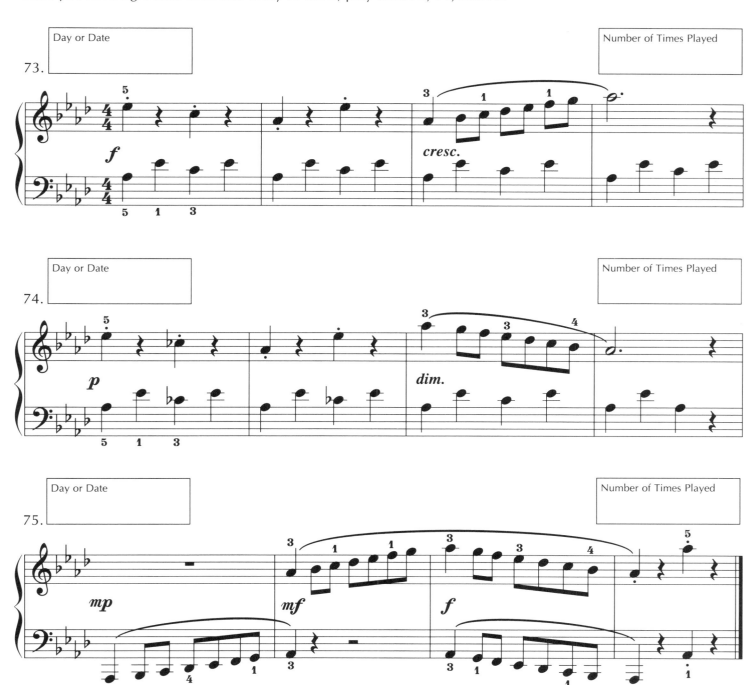

Daily Note Search

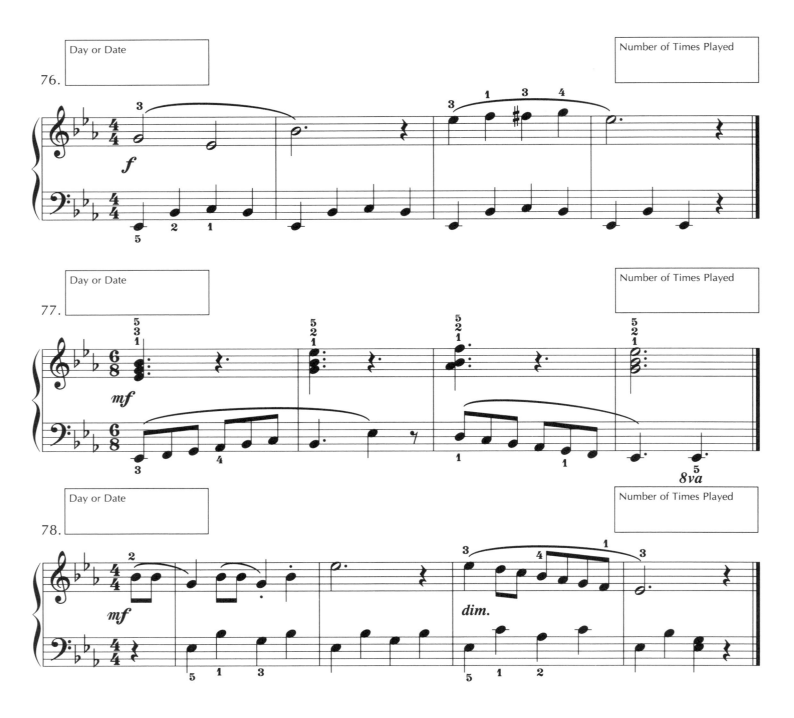

Daily Note Search

After you have sight read each line a day as usual, play lines 79, 80, and 81 without stopping.

Day or Date	Number of Times Played

79.

Day or Date	Number of Times Played

80.

Day or Date	Number of Times Played

81.

Daily Note Search

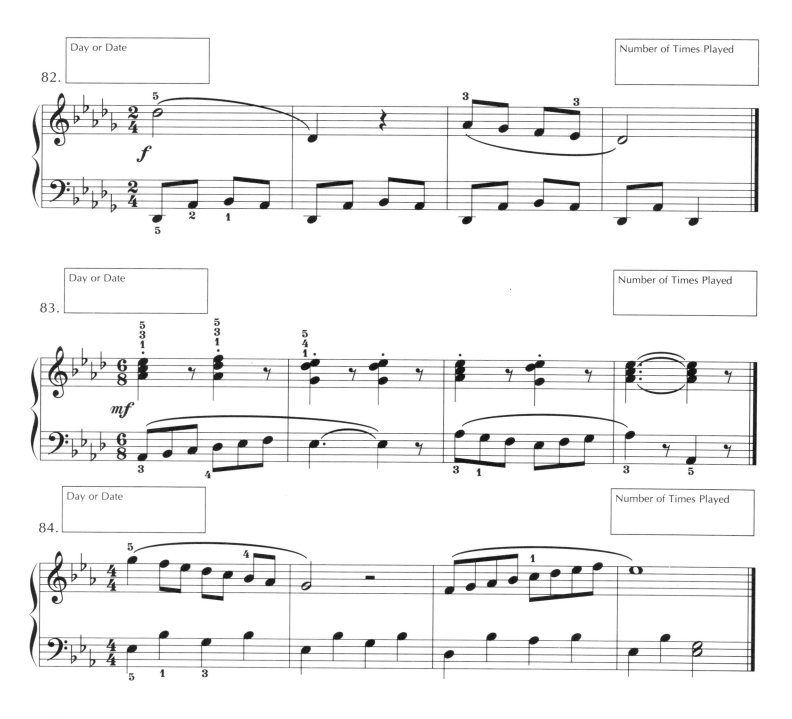

82.
Day or Date

Number of Times Played

83.
Day or Date

Number of Times Played

84.
Day or Date

Number of Times Played

Daily Note Search

Sight Reading Certificate

for

_____

who has completed Level 4 with

> *Honors*
>
> *Superior Honors*

Date_____

Teacher_____

*Honors and Superior Honors stickers are available from your favorite music store. Ask for Jane Smisor Bastien Seals, *Honor Awards* (G2).